IMAGINE

an illustrated journal

ALL ARTWORK BY CYNTHIA LOUDEN

All things are perfect, exactly as they are!   –Buddha

How wonderful! How wonderful!

Memory is a child
walking along the seashore.
You never can tell
what small pebble
it will pick up
and store away
among its
treasured things.

- Pierce Harris

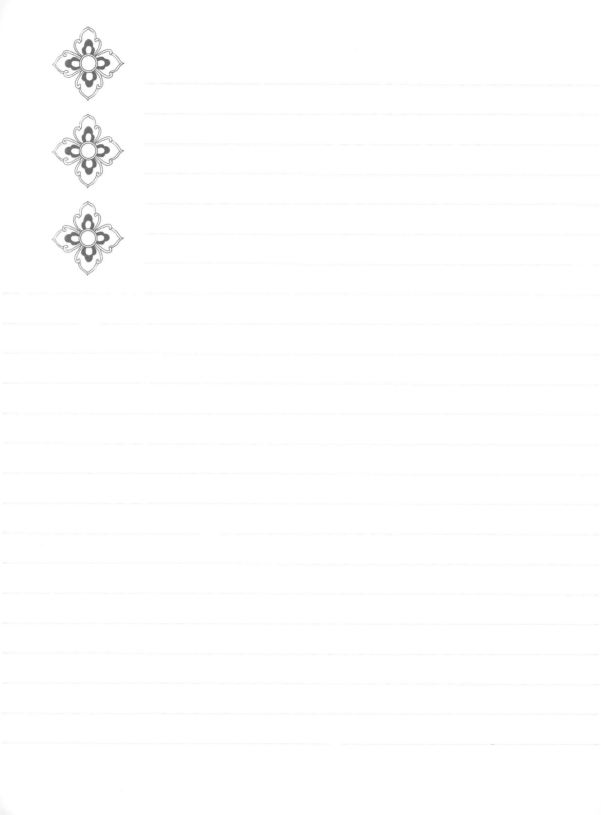

The joy of a spirit
is the measure of its power.

-Ninon de Lenclos

If we could *see*
the miracle
of a single flower
clearly;
our whole *life*
would
change.

-*Buddha*

Nature often holds up a mirror so we can see more clearly

the ongoing processes of growth, renewal, and transformation in our lives. — Mary Ann Brussat

Joy in looking and comprehending is nature's *most beautiful* gift. *–Albert Einstein*

If nothing ever changed there would be no butterflies.

Each friend represents a world in us, a world possibly not born until they arrive,

...and it is only by this meeting that a new world is born.

-Anais Nin

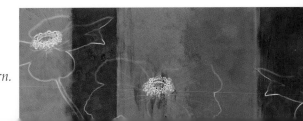

Each morning we are born again.
What we do today is what matters most.

–Buddha

Believe there are no limits but the sky.   *–Cervantes*

Be patient with all that is unresolved in your heart.

And try to love the questions themselves. -Rainer Maria Rilke

Be aware of what is in you.
Announce it, pronounce it,
produce it and give birth to it.

-Meister Eckhart

or in the life of another. -Helen Keller

When we do the best that we can, we never know what miracle is wrought in our life, or in the life of another. -Helen Keller

One
change
leaves
the way open
for the
introduction
of others.

-Niccolo Machiavelli

Patience is the companion *of wisdom.* –Saint Augustine

While
they were
saying
among
themselves
it cannot
be done,
it was done.

-Helen Keller

One flower can wake the dream.

If you have anything

really valuable

to contribute *to the world*

it will come through

the expression

of your own personality,

that single spark

of divinity

that sets you off

and makes you different

from every other living *creature.*

–Bruce Barton

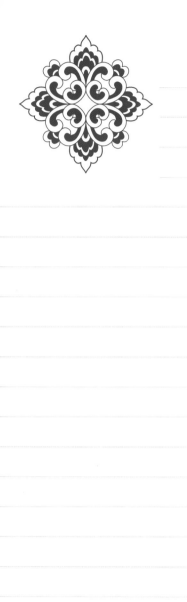

Music

in the

soul

can be

heard

by the

universe.

-Lao-Tzu

Wherever you go,
go with all your heart

-Confuscious

Just remain
in the center,
watching.
And then forget
that you are there.

-Lao-Tzu

The art of life is a constant readjustment to our surroundings.   –Kakuzo Okakaura

I do not
understand
the mystery
of grace-
only that it
meets us
where we are,
but does not
leave us
where it
found us.

–Anne LaMott

Wisdom begins in wonder.

–Socrates

Wisdom tells me
I am nothing.
Love tells me
I am everything.
And between
the two
my life
flows.

-Nisargadatta Maharaj

As soon as you trust yourself, you will know how to live.   -Johann Wolfgang von Goethe

Not Truth,
but Faith
it is
that keeps
the world
alive.

-Edna St. Vincent Millay

The butterfly *counts not months but moments and has* time *enough.*   *–Rabindranath Tagore*

You must learn to be still
in the midst of activity

and to be vibrantly alive in repose.

–Indira Gandhi

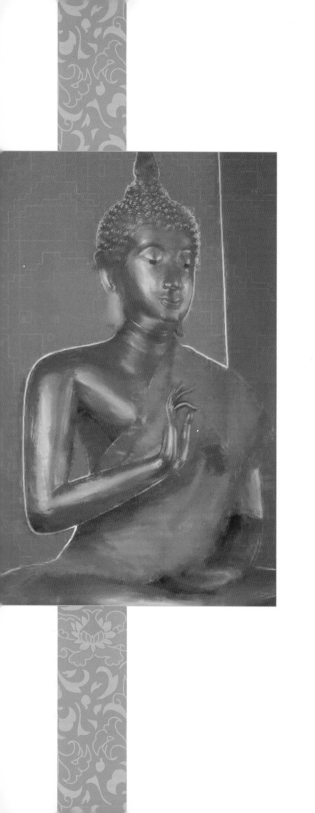

The
dedicated
life
is the life
worth living.
You must give
with your
whole
heart.

-Annie Dillard

*Cynthia Louden
merges photography and painting,
the concrete and the obscure,
and the known and the unknown
to create
a wonderfully heightened
sense of reality.*

All artwork by Cynthia Louden.
Book design by Liz Kalloch.